TELL ME iF YOU LiKE...

GÉRARD GRÉVERAND

ILLUSTRATED BY MAGALI BARDOS

Pavilion Children's Books

For Samuel, Tom, Pablo, Alix, Antoine and Inès.

The little things that make us happy are like magical moments.
Our five senses dwell upon these experiences before
tucking them safely away forever in our memories.
Everyday smells, tastes and colours create impressions that
strike a chord in a way that is sometimes difficult to explain.
They become associated with your first steps through life,
like countless little pebbles strewn along the way.
In lingering for a few seconds on these special moments
you realize what you like and don't like, and this way you
get to know yourself better. Saying what you like is a bit like
writing your own story or painting a picture of yourself.

TELL ME IF YOU LIKE...

WAKING UP THINKING THAT
IT'S TUESDAY OR THURSDAY
AND THEN REALIZING
THAT IT'S SUNDAY

TELL ME IF YOU LIKE...

WALKING IN THE SNOW OR ON A SANDY BEACH
AND MAKING YOUR FOOTPRINTS AS BIG AS
YOU CAN SO THAT PEOPLE THINK A MONSTER
OR A GIANT HAS LEFT ITS TRACKS THERE

TELL ME iF YOU LiKE...

BLOCKING A LADYBIRD'S PATH SO THAT
IT ENDS UP CRAWLING OVER YOUR HAND

TELL ME IF YOU LIKE...

LICKING THE TOPPING OFF ICED BUNS

TELL ME IF YOU LIKE...

MAKING SPIT BUBBLES

TELL ME IF YOU LIKE...

HOOVERING YOUR TUMMY OR YOUR ARM

TELL ME IF YOU LIKE...

WAKING UP IN THE MIDDLE OF THE NIGHT, COSY AND WARM IN YOUR BED, LISTENING TO THE STORM OUTSIDE AS THE WIND RAGES FURIOUSLY AROUND THE ROOF AND THE RAIN BATTERS THE WINDOWS

TELL ME IF YOU LIKE...

TRYING NOT TO BLINK OR SWALLOW FOR AS LONG AS YOU CAN

TELL ME IF YOU LIKE...

SMELLING YOUR MUM'S HAIR WHEN SHE'S JUST HAD IT DONE AT THE HAIRDRESSER'S

TELL ME IF YOU LIKE...

PRETENDING YOU CAN SPEAK FRENCH

TELL ME IF YOU LIKE...

CURLING UP UNDER THE COVERS
IN BED AND PRETENDING
YOU ARE IN A TENT

TELL ME IF YOU LIKE...
PUTTING A WHOLE ICE CUBE IN YOUR MOUTH
AND TRYING TO SPEAK AT THE SAME TIME

TELL ME IF YOU LIKE...
WOBBLING A LOOSE TOOTH
WITH YOUR TONGUE

TELL ME IF YOU LIKE...
EATING SATSUMAS AND KEEPING
THE PIPS IN YOUR MOUTH SO YOU CAN
SPIT THEM ALL OUT AT ONCE

TELL ME IF YOU LIKE...
RUMMAGING ABOUT IN YOUR NOSE
FOR THE BIGGEST BOGEY

TELL ME IF YOU LIKE...
FINDING A TOY YOU THOUGHT YOU HAD LOST

TELL ME IF YOU LIKE...
GOING CROSS-EYED IN FRONT OF THE MIRROR

WOODEN FLOOR

TELL ME IF YOU LIKE...

SWALLOWING HALF A BIG, JUICY CHERRY

1. THAT THERE IS
A MAGGOT HOLE IN
THE LEFT-OVER HALF

AND THEN NOTICING:

2. THAT YOU HAVE PROBABLY
SWALLOWED THE MAGGOT
THAT LIVED THERE...

TELL ME IF YOU LIKE...

HAVING A

TELL ME IF YOU LIKE...

SMELLING THE AIR AFTER FIREWORKS HAVE EXPLODED

TELL ME IF YOU LIKE...

GOING OVER A BUMP IN THE ROAD AND FEELING YOUR TUMMY DO A TRIPLE SOMERSAULT

TELL ME IF YOU LIKE...

PRETENDING YOU ARE A DEEP-SEA DIVER

TELL ME IF YOU LIKE...

WATCHING THE MAN WHO
HAS COME TO FIX THE TV
OR THE WASHING MACHINE

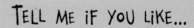

TELL ME IF YOU LIKE...

WAITING TILL A MOSQUITO
IS JUST ABOUT TO BITE YOU
SO THAT YOU CAN SQUASH IT
FLAT WITH YOUR HAND

TELL ME IF YOU LIKE...

GOING
THROUGH
A TUNNEL

TELL ME IF YOU LIKE...

BITING INTO AN OR A WITH YOUR SHUT AND LISTENING TO THE SOUND IT MAKES AND WONDERING IF ANYONE ELSE CAN HEAR IT TOO

TELL ME IF YOU LIKE...
SPENDING **AGES** IN THE SHOWER

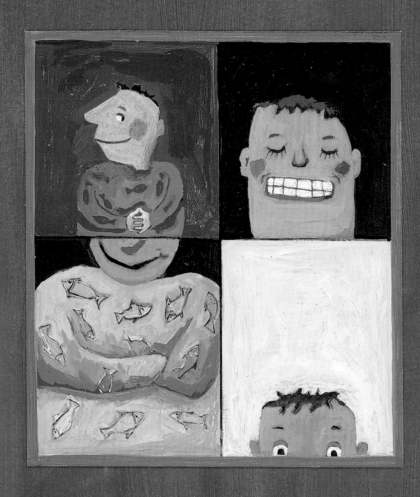

TELL ME IF YOU LIKE...

HAVING YOUR PICTURE TAKEN
IN A PHOTO BOOTH

Tell me if you like...

Sneezing five times in a row

A

AND

GETTING

LOUDER AND

LOUDER AND

LOUDER

TELL ME IF YOU LIKE...
PLAYING MONOPOLY AND BUYING UP
PARK LANE AND MAYFAIR AND BUILDING
FOUR HOUSES AND A HOTEL ON THEM

TELL ME IF YOU LIKE...
IMAGINING WHAT LIFE WILL BE LIKE FOR PEOPLE
IN 245 MILLION YEARS

TELL ME IF YOU LIKE...
EATING GRAPES AND PUTTING AS MANY AS YOU CAN IN YOUR MOUTH
SO YOU CAN CHOMP THEM ALL IN ONE GO

TELL ME IF YOU LIKE...
EATING ONLY THE MELTED
CHEESE ON CHEESE-ON-TOAST

TELL ME IF YOU LIKE...

WALKING ON THE EDGE OF THE PAVEMENT AS IF IT WERE
A TIGHTROPE SUSPENDED SEVEN METRES FROM THE GROUND

TELL ME IF YOU LIKE...

CLIMBING TO THE TOP OF A LADDER OR A TREE

TELL ME IF YOU LIKE...

TRYING TO WIGGLE YOUR EARS WITHOUT MOVING YOUR EYES OR EYEBROWS

TELL ME IF YOU LIKE...

PEELING AN APPLE OR AN ORANGE IN ONE GO SO THAT THE PEEL ENDS UP AS ONE LONG SPIRAL

TELL ME IF YOU LIKE...

DOING A WEE OR A POO
IN THE TOILET
AND WATCHING WHAT HAPPENS
WHEN YOU FLUSH

TELL ME IF YOU LIKE...

CLOSING YOUR EYES
AS TIGHT AS POSSIBLE
SO THAT A KALEIDOSCOPE OF
COLOUR AND LIGHT APPEARS
BEHIND YOUR EYELIDS

TELL ME IF YOU LIKE...

KISSING YOUR
DAD WHEN HE
HASN'T SHAVED

TELL ME IF YOU LIKE...

SMELLING YOUR FAVOURITE
CAKE BAKING AWAY
IN THE OVEN

TELL ME iF YOU LiKE...

FINDING THE SILVER SIXPENCE IN THE
CHRISTMAS PUDDING

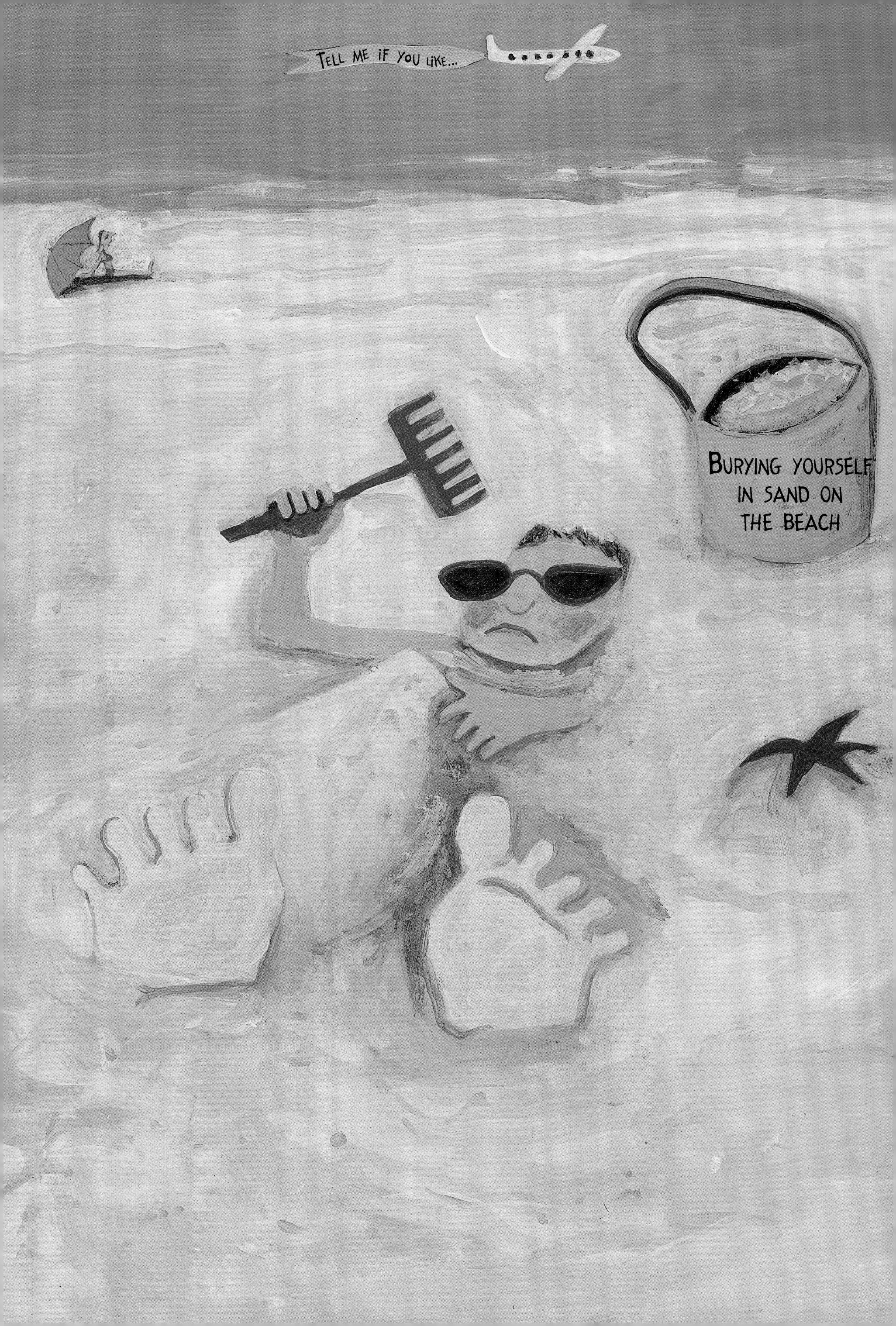
TELL ME IF YOU LIKE...
BURYING YOURSELF IN SAND ON THE BEACH

TELL ME IF YOU LIKE...

DRINKING A FIZZY DRINK
REALLY FAST AND
FEELING THE BUBBLES
GO UP YOUR NOSE

TELL ME IF YOU LIKE...

DRAGGING YOUR FEET IN
AUTUMN LEAVES SO THAT
YOU CAN HEAR THEM
CRACKLE AS YOU WALK

TELL ME IF YOU LIKE...

USING YOUR KNIFE AND FORK
AS DRUMSTICKS ON
THE GLASSES, THE TABLE
AND THE PLATES

TELL ME IF YOU LIKE...

IMAGINING YOU ARE A FAMOUS
INTERNATIONAL ADVENTURE HERO.
ARE YOU A PIRATE OR
A DETECTIVE, A MAD SCIENTIST
OR A SPY?
ARE YOU ROBIN HOOD?

TELL ME IF YOU LIKE...

MAKING TRACKS IN
YOUR MASHED POTATO WITH
YOUR FORK, POURING OUT
A LAKE OF GRAVY IN THE MIDDLE
AND THEN OPENING THE
FLOODGATES SO THAT IT SPILLS
OUT OVER THE ROADS

TELL ME IF YOU LIKE...

CHECKING UNDERNEATH
THE BED BEFORE
YOU GO TO SLEEP

FINDING YOUR WAY WITH A TORCH WHEN THERE IS A POWERCUT

TELL ME IF YOU LIKE...

LETTING YOUR DOG SLEEP IN YOUR BED

TELL ME IF YOU LIKE...
SUCKING UP SPAGHETTI WITHOUT MAKING
THE SLIGHTEST NOISE

TELL ME IF YOU LIKE...
MAKING AN ENORMOUS BUBBLE-GUM
BUBBLE AND GETTING IT TO GO BACK INTO YOUR MOUTH BEFORE IT
BURSTS AND STICKS TO YOUR CHIN, YOUR NOSE AND YOUR CHEEKS

TELL ME IF YOU LIKE...
SPENDING AGES
MAKING BUBBLES
IN YOUR MILK AND
THEN DRINKING IT

TELL ME IF YOU LIKE...
DAZZLING SOMEONE WITH
THE SUN'S REFLECTION OFF YOUR WATCH

TELL ME IF YOU LIKE...

SMELLING THE WARM, WET
ROAD AFTER A STORM AND
WATCHING STEAM RISE FROM IT

TELL ME IF YOU LIKE...

DOODLING ON THE WINDOWPANE
WHEN IT'S COVERED IN CONDENSATION

TELL ME IF YOU LIKE...

IMAGINING YOU HAVE BEEN LOCKED
OVERNIGHT IN A TOY SHOP,
CAKE SHOP OR A MUSEUM
AND YOU ARE ABLE TO DO
ANYTHING YOU WANT

TELL ME IF YOU LIKE...

LETTING
GO OF THE
HANDLEBARS

TELL ME IF YOU LIKE...

WATCHING A FILM OR CARTOON
FOR THE TENTH TIME AND
SAYING THE ACTORS' LINES
OUT LOUD AT EXACTLY
THE SAME TIME AS THEM

TELL ME IF YOU LIKE...

LOOKING AT PHOTOS OF YOUR PARENTS WHEN THEY WERE LITTLE

TELL ME IF YOU LIKE...

STARING AT THE MOON UNTIL YOU SEE TOWNS AND OCEANS, ROADS AND BUILDINGS...

TELL ME IF YOU LIKE...

SNIFFING FLOWERS AS HARD AS YOU CAN SO THAT THE PETALS STICK TO YOUR NOSE

TELL ME IF YOU LIKE...

GOING DOWN THE SLIDE HEAD FIRST

Tell me if you like...

Seeing the words

THE END

when a film

or a book

is finished

Tell me if you like...

Being asked
what you like

First published in Great Britain in 2002 by
Pavilion Children's Books
A member of Chrysalis Books plc
64 Brewery Road
London N7 9NT
www.chrysalisbooks.co.uk

First edition: copyright © 2000 by Nathan / HER, Paris – France.
Current edition: copyright © 2001 by Nathan / VUEF, Paris – France.
Original edition: *Dis-moi si tu aimes*
Translated by Colette Hanley

A CIP catalogue record for this book is available
from the British Library.
ISBN: 1 84365 010 X
2 4 6 8 10 9 7 5 3
Printed in France by Pollina, n° L88418